MULTIPLICATIO TABLES - UGH!

Millions of schoolchildren have been told by hundreds of thousands of adults that they need to know their tables.

At some time, someone must have said to you, "You need to know your tables by heart!" And you must have spent hours of time in your school life doing mathematics where, quite often, you need to know the answer to 'three sevens' or 'six sixes' or 'seven eights'.

So did your great-grandmother!

Some people learn their tables easily and quickly as part of their ordinary school mathematics. Other people – no less clever – find that they cannot remember them without some extra effort and practice

$$1 \times 10 =$$
$$7 \times 8 =$$
$$11 \times 7 =$$
$$9 \times 8 =$$

Since you have a copy of this book, it seems as though you might be one of those who needs some of that extra effort and practice – so let's see what is involved.

Turn over and see just how many tables there are to be learnt –

1

$1 \times 2 = 2$	$1 \times 3 = 3$	$1 \times 4 = 4$
$2 \times 2 = 4$	$2 \times 3 = 6$	$2 \times 4 = 8$
$3 \times 2 = 6$	$3 \times 3 = 9$	$3 \times 4 = 12$
$4 \times 2 = 8$	$4 \times 3 = 12$	$4 \times 4 = 16$
$5 \times 2 = 10$	$5 \times 3 = 15$	$5 \times 4 = 20$
$6 \times 2 = 12$	$6 \times 3 = 18$	$6 \times 4 = 24$
$7 \times 2 = 14$	$7 \times 3 = 21$	$7 \times 4 = 28$
$8 \times 2 = 16$	$8 \times 3 = 24$	$8 \times 4 = 32$
$9 \times 2 = 18$	$9 \times 3 = 27$	$9 \times 4 = 36$
$10 \times 2 = 20$	$10 \times 3 = 30$	$10 \times 4 = 40$
$11 \times 2 = 22$	$11 \times 3 = 33$	$11 \times 4 = 44$
$12 \times 2 = 24$	$12 \times 3 = 36$	$12 \times 4 = 48$
$1 \times 5 = 5$	$1 \times 6 = 6$	$1 \times 7 = 7$
$2 \times 5 = 10$	$2 \times 6 = 12$	$2 \times 7 = 14$
$3 \times 5 = 15$	$3 \times 6 = 18$	$3 \times 7 = 21$
$4 \times 5 = 20$	$4 \times 6 = 24$	$4 \times 7 = 28$
$5 \times 5 = 25$	$5 \times 6 = 30$	$5 \times 7 = 35$
$6 \times 5 = 30$	$6 \times 6 = 36$	$6 \times 7 = 42$
$7 \times 5 = 35$	$7 \times 6 = 42$	$7 \times 7 = 49$
$8 \times 5 = 40$	$8 \times 6 = 48$	$8 \times 7 = 56$
$9 \times 5 = 45$	$9 \times 6 = 54$	$9 \times 7 = 63$
$10 \times 5 = 50$	$10 \times 6 = 60$	$10 \times 7 = 70$
$11 \times 5 = 55$	$11 \times 6 = 66$	$11 \times 7 = 77$
$12 \times 5 = 60$	$12 \times 6 = 72$	$12 \times 7 = 84$

$1 \times 8 = 8$	$1 \times 9 = 9$	$1 \times 10 = 10$
$2 \times 8 = 16$	$2 \times 9 = 18$	$2 \times 10 = 20$
$3 \times 8 = 24$	$3 \times 9 = 27$	$3 \times 10 = 30$
$4 \times 8 = 32$	$4 \times 9 = 36$	$4 \times 10 = 40$
$5 \times 8 = 40$	$5 \times 9 = 45$	$5 \times 10 = 50$
$6 \times 8 = 48$	$6 \times 9 = 54$	$6 \times 10 = 60$
$7 \times 8 = 56$	$7 \times 9 = 63$	$7 \times 10 = 70$
$8 \times 8 = 64$	$8 \times 9 = 72$	$8 \times 10 = 80$
$9 \times 8 = 72$	$9 \times 9 = 81$	$9 \times 10 = 90$
$10 \times 8 = 80$	$10 \times 9 = 90$	$10 \times 10 = 100$
$11 \times 8 = 88$	$11 \times 9 = 99$	$11 \times 10 = 110$
$12 \times 8 = 96$	$12 \times 9 = 108$	$12 \times 10 = 120$

$1 \times 11 = 11$	$1 \times 12 = 12$
$2 \times 11 = 22$	$2 \times 12 = 24$
$3 \times 11 = 33$	$3 \times 12 = 36$
$4 \times 11 = 44$	$4 \times 12 = 48$
$5 \times 11 = 55$	$5 \times 12 = 60$
$6 \times 11 = 66$	$6 \times 12 = 72$
$7 \times 11 = 77$	$7 \times 12 = 84$
$8 \times 11 = 88$	$8 \times 12 = 96$
$9 \times 11 = 99$	$9 \times 12 = 108$
$10 \times 11 = 110$	$10 \times 12 = 120$
$11 \times 11 = 121$	$11 \times 12 = 132$
$12 \times 11 = 132$	$12 \times 12 = 144$

A little counting will show you that there are eleven tables, and each of the tables contains twelve number facts. Altogether, there are 132 things to learn.

But really the job is easier than that – much easier.

To start with, you don't really have to **learn** these. You know them already!

$1 \times 2 = 2$
$1 \times 3 = 3$
$1 \times 4 = 4$
$1 \times 5 = 5$
$1 \times 6 = 6$
$1 \times 7 = 7$
$1 \times 8 = 8$
$1 \times 9 = 9$
$1 \times 10 = 10$
$1 \times 11 = 11$
$1 \times 12 = 12$

So there are no longer 132 lines to be learnt, but 121.

If you look back again at the tables printed out on pages 1, 2 and 3, you will see that many of them are **doubles.**

That is, the same number fact appears in two different tables. For example, in the two times table $3 \times 2 = 6$ And in the three times table $2 \times 3 = 6$

There is no need to learn the same fact twice, and so this makes the job easier.

You will find that there are 55 of these doubles in the multiplication tables.

So there are no longer 121 facts to be learnt, only 66, less than half the number we started with!

On the next pages you can see the tables where the doubles appear. They have been printed in colour, along with the eleven easy lines.

$1 \times 2 = 2$	$1 \times 3 = 3$	$1 \times 4 = 4$
$2 \times 2 = 4$	$2 \times 3 = 6$	$2 \times 4 = 8$
$3 \times 2 = 6$	$3 \times 3 = 9$	$3 \times 4 = 12$
$4 \times 2 = 8$	$4 \times 3 = 12$	$4 \times 4 = 16$
$5 \times 2 = 10$	$5 \times 3 = 15$	$5 \times 4 = 20$
$6 \times 2 = 12$	$6 \times 3 = 18$	$6 \times 4 = 24$
$7 \times 2 = 14$	$7 \times 3 = 21$	$7 \times 4 = 28$
$8 \times 2 = 16$	$8 \times 3 = 24$	$8 \times 4 = 32$
$9 \times 2 = 18$	$9 \times 3 = 27$	$9 \times 4 = 36$
$10 \times 2 = 20$	$10 \times 3 = 30$	$10 \times 4 = 40$
$11 \times 2 = 22$	$11 \times 3 = 33$	$11 \times 4 = 44$
$12 \times 2 = 24$	$12 \times 3 = 36$	$12 \times 4 = 48$
$1 \times 5 = 5$	$1 \times 6 = 6$	$1 \times 7 = 7$
$2 \times 5 = 10$	$2 \times 6 = 12$	$2 \times 7 = 14$
$3 \times 5 = 15$	$3 \times 6 = 18$	$3 \times 7 = 21$
$4 \times 5 = 20$	$4 \times 6 = 24$	$4 \times 7 = 28$
$5 \times 5 = 25$	$5 \times 6 = 30$	$5 \times 7 = 35$
$6 \times 5 = 30$	$6 \times 6 = 36$	$6 \times 7 = 42$
$7 \times 5 = 35$	$7 \times 6 = 42$	$7 \times 7 = 49$
$8 \times 5 = 40$	$8 \times 6 = 48$	$8 \times 7 = 56$
$9 \times 5 = 45$	$9 \times 6 = 54$	$9 \times 7 = 63$
$10 \times 5 = 50$	$10 \times 6 = 60$	$10 \times 7 = 70$
$11 \times 5 = 55$	$11 \times 6 = 66$	$11 \times 7 = 77$
$12 \times 5 = 60$	$12 \times 6 = 72$	$12 \times 7 = 84$

$1 \times 8 = 8$	$1 \times 9 = 9$	$1 \times 10 = 10$
$2 \times 8 = 16$	$2 \times 9 = 18$	$2 \times 10 = 20$
$3 \times 8 = 24$	$3 \times 9 = 27$	$3 \times 10 = 30$
$4 \times 8 = 32$	$4 \times 9 = 36$	$4 \times 10 = 40$
$5 \times 8 = 40$	$5 \times 9 = 45$	$5 \times 10 = 50$
$6 \times 8 = 48$	$6 \times 9 = 54$	$6 \times 10 = 60$
$7 \times 8 = 56$	$7 \times 9 = 63$	$7 \times 10 = 70$
$8 \times 8 = 64$	$8 \times 9 = 72$	$8 \times 10 = 80$
$9 \times 8 = 72$	$9 \times 9 = 81$	$9 \times 10 = 90$
$10 \times 8 = 80$	$10 \times 9 = 90$	$10 \times 10 = 100$
$11 \times 8 = 88$	$11 \times 9 = 99$	$11 \times 10 = 110$
$12 \times 8 = 96$	$12 \times 9 = 108$	$12 \times 10 = 120$

$1 \times 11 = 11$	$1 \times 12 = 12$
$2 \times 11 = 22$	$2 \times 12 = 24$
$3 \times 11 = 33$	$3 \times 12 = 36$
$4 \times 11 = 44$	$4 \times 12 = 48$
$5 \times 11 = 55$	$5 \times 12 = 60$
$6 \times 11 = 66$	$6 \times 12 = 72$
$7 \times 11 = 77$	$7 \times 12 = 84$
$8 \times 11 = 88$	$8 \times 12 = 96$
$9 \times 11 = 99$	$9 \times 12 = 108$
$10 \times 11 = 110$	$10 \times 12 = 120$
$11 \times 11 = 121$	$11 \times 12 = 132$
$12 \times 11 = 132$	$12 \times 12 = 144$

TAKE RED AS HAVING BEEN READ

Before you check whether you know these 66 facts or not, it may be possible to make the job even easier.

You must surely know your two times table.

$$2 \times 2 = 4$$
$$3 \times 2 = 6$$
$$4 \times 2 = 8$$
$$5 \times 2 = 10$$
$$6 \times 2 = 12$$
$$7 \times 2 = 14$$
$$8 \times 2 = 16$$
$$9 \times 2 = 18$$
$$10 \times 2 = 20$$
$$11 \times 2 = 22$$
$$12 \times 2 = 24$$

If we take away those eleven lines from the 66 we had left, there are only 55 still to learn.

What else might you be sure of already?

$$10 \times 3 = 30$$
$$10 \times 4 = 40$$
$$10 \times 5 = 50$$
$$10 \times 6 = 60$$
$$10 \times 7 = 70$$
$$10 \times 8 = 80$$
$$10 \times 9 = 90$$
$$10 \times 10 = 100$$

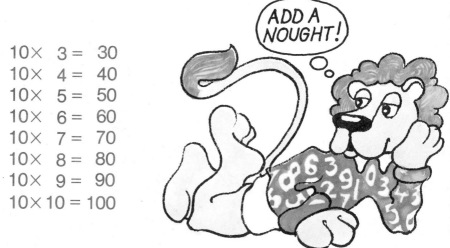

If you know these, there are just 47 still to learn.

Most children quickly recognise the pattern in the
eleven times table, and we can soon be sure of these

$11 \times 3 = 33$
$11 \times 4 = 44$
$11 \times 5 = 55$
$11 \times 6 = 66$
$11 \times 7 = 77$
$11 \times 8 = 88$
$11 \times 9 = 99$
$11 \times 10 = 110$

With these eight lines thoroughly learnt, there are **39**
still to come.

Here is a list of those 39 remaining lines which need to be thoroughly learnt

$3 \times 3 = 9$
$4 \times 3 = 12$
$5 \times 3 = 15$
$6 \times 3 = 18$
$7 \times 3 = 21$
$8 \times 3 = 24$
$9 \times 3 = 27$
$12 \times 3 = 36$

$4 \times 4 = 16$
$5 \times 4 = 20$
$6 \times 4 = 24$
$7 \times 4 = 28$
$8 \times 4 = 32$
$9 \times 4 = 36$
$12 \times 4 = 48$

$5 \times 5 = 25$
$6 \times 5 = 30$
$7 \times 5 = 35$
$8 \times 5 = 40$
$9 \times 5 = 45$
$12 \times 5 = 60$

$6 \times 6 = 36$
$7 \times 6 = 42$
$8 \times 6 = 48$
$9 \times 6 = 54$
$12 \times 6 = 72$

$7 \times 7 = 49$
$8 \times 7 = 56$
$9 \times 7 = 63$
$12 \times 7 = 84$

$8 \times 8 = 64$
$9 \times 8 = 72$
$12 \times 8 = 96$

$9 \times 9 = 81$
$12 \times 9 = 108$

$12 \times 10 = 120$
$11 \times 11 = 121$
$12 \times 11 = 132$

$12 \times 12 = 144$

LEARN THESE!

39 lines which you may not yet be quite sure of! Suppose you could only manage to learn one a day, it would still mean that in just over a month you would know them **all** . . .

Yet some boys and girls have been going to school year after YEAR after YEAR, and still never really bother to learn all their tables thoroughly.

Don't let tables beat you any longer!

On the next few pages, there are some speed tests for you to try out. Use a watch with a second hand and time yourself. Aim to do each of the tests several times, increasing your speed more and more.

Don't spend more than a few minutes at a time doing this.

Make up your mind, right now, that you are going to know all your tables perfectly, and that you are going to know them perfectly within the next few weeks.

YOU CAN DO IT, LET BATTLE COMMENCE

SPEED TESTS

3×3	4×3	4× 2	11×10
8×5	2×4	2× 8	10×10
11×2	5×4	10× 2	11× 8
7×4	11×4	8× 4	10× 9
9×4	10×5	10× 4	12× 9
5×2	7×7	10× 6	8× 3
6×5	6×6	6×11	9× 5
12×4	5×5	7× 3	7× 9
9×2	6×4	11× 3	4× 8
4×4	8×6	7×11	9× 4
12×3	7×5	12× 8	8× 7
9×3	6×7	11× 9	12× 7
10×7	2×6	11×11	7× 6
12×6	5×3	12×12	9× 8
3×2	7×2	8× 8	9× 9
12×2	9×6	9× 8	7× 5
10×3	11×5	9× 9	12× 4
8×3	8×7	12×11	8× 5
12×5	12×7	10×12	10× 8
6×3	9×5	8×10	11×11

How many 10s in 50?   How many 10s in 110?

How many 9s in 45?   How many 12s in 96?

How many 11s in 77?   How many 3s in 27?

How many 5s in 25?   How many 10s in 30?

How many 3s in 36?   How many 9s in 18?

How many 8s in 64?   How many 3s in 18?

How many 9s in 90?   How many 11s in 88?

How many 7s in 49?   How many 9s in 99?

How many 8s in 32?   How many 12s in 132?

How many 6s in 42?   How many 12s in 144?

How many 4s in 44?   How many 10s in 120?

How many 12s in 60?   How many 11s in 22?

How many 7s in 14?   How many 8s in 48?

How many 10s in 100?   How many 6s in 54?

How many 6s in 30?   How many 10s in 60?

How many 7s in 70?   How many 11s in 99?

How many 3s in 33?   How many 6s in 36?

How many 4s in 16?   How many 2s in 10?

How many 2s in 16?   How many 4s in 40?

How many 5s in 20?   How many 6s in 66?

Find the missing numbers:

$2 \times ? = 4$	$? \times 5 = 55$	$4 \times ? = 16$
$2 \times ? = 20$	$3 \times ? = 6$	$? \times 6 = 36$
$? \times 8 = 40$	$7 \times ? = 21$	$4 \times ? = 12$
$9 \times 3 = ?$	$3 \times ? = 24$	$? \times 5 = 30$
$3 \times ? = 36$	$8 \times ? = 16$	$7 \times ? = 77$
$8 \times ? = 96$	$2 \times ? = 12$	$? \times 8 = 64$
$12 \times 7 = ?$	$2 \times ? = 24$	$12 \times ? = 132$
$7 \times ? = 49$	$7 \times ? = 28$	$? \times 12 = 120$
$10 \times ? = 70$	$6 \times ? = 66$	$5 \times ? = 60$
$9 \times ? = 81$	$9 \times ? = 63$	$? \times 8 = 48$
$11 \times ? = 33$	$10 \times ? = 90$	$4 \times ? = 40$
$8 \times ? = 88$	$12 \times ? = 144$	$2 \times ? = 18$
$12 \times ? = 108$	$? \times 3 = 15$	$? \times 7 = 35$
$11 \times 9 = ?$	$? \times 8 = 80$	$? \times 5 = 55$
$6 \times ? = 60$	$7 \times ? = 56$	$10 \times ? = 110$
$9 \times ? = 54$	$? \times 5 = 25$	$? \times 3 = 18$
$6 \times ? = 42$	$9 \times ? = 36$	$6 \times ? = 18$
$? \times 4 = 28$	$4 \times ? = 44$	$10 \times ? = 30$
$4 \times ? = 24$	$12 \times ? = 72$	$? \times 3 = 21$
$4 \times ? = 48$	$5 \times ? = 60$	$5 \times ? = 20$

What two numbers multiplied together make:

6	8	48	88
16	10	49	90
20	99	50	96
24	14	54	100
28	15	55	108
48	16	56	110
72	18	60	120
60	20	63	121
70	22	64	132
84	24	65	144
88	27	66	33
96	28	70	66

How many numbers can you find that will divide into these exactly?

16 (try for 3)	32 (try for 4)
18 (try for 3)	48 (try for 8)
24 (try for 5)	54 (try for 4)
30 (try for 5)	36 (try for 6)

A final check on your speeds – how quickly can you do each column? Miss out the ones you can't do at once – and then go back and learn them!

2× 6 =	3× 2 =	4× 2 =	5× 2 =
4× 6 =	7× 2 =	8× 2 =	9× 2 =
10× 2 =	11× 2 =	12× 2 =	3× 3 =
4× 3 =	5× 3 =	6× 3 =	7× 3 =
8× 3 =	9× 3 =	10× 3 =	11× 3 =
12× 3 =	4× 4 =	5× 4 =	6× 4 =
7× 4 =	8× 4 =	9× 4 =	10× 4 =
11× 4 =	12× 4 =	5× 5 =	6× 5 =
7× 5 =	8× 5 =	9× 5 =	10× 5 =
11× 5 =	12× 5 =	6× 6 =	7× 6 =
8× 6 =	9× 6 =	10× 6 =	11× 6 =
12× 6 =	7× 7 =	8× 7 =	9× 7 =
10× 7 =	11× 7 =	12× 7 =	8× 8 =
9× 8 =	10× 8 =	11× 8 =	12× 8 =
9× 9 =	10× 9 =	11× 9 =	12× 9 =
10× 10 =	11× 10 =	12× 10 =	11× 11 =
12× 12 =	5× 6 =	5× 8 =	5× 9 =
5× 11 =	5× 12 =	6× 7 =	6× 8 =
6× 9 =	6× 12 =	7× 8 =	7× 9 =
11× 7 =	7× 12 =	8× 9 =	12× 9 =

NOW TURN THE TABLES ON YOUR FRIENDS

Text © 1976 Arthur Razzell
Illustrations © 1976 Macmillan Education
Published by Macmillan Education Ltd
Basingstoke and London
First published 1976
Reprinted
1976, 1977, 1978, 1979, 1981, 1983, 1986, 1988, 1989